WALLACE AND THE FIREWORKS

Text by James Drummond
Illustrations by Louise Annand

This book is dedicated to
Susan Millar, with love.

The author acknowledges the help and advice given by the Strathclyde Fire Brigade and hopes that the book may contribute towards their "safe fireworks" campaign.

Other books in the series

Wallace the Fire Dog
Wallace's School Adventure
Wallace Loses his Boots

Published in 1991 by
The Amaising Publishing House Ltd.
Musselburgh
EH21 7UJ
Scotland

031-665 8237

ISBN 1 871512 25 5

Printed & Bound by Scotprint Ltd, Musselburgh

Wallace was a brave dog. Even when he was a very small puppy living in a comfortable house in the West End of Glasgow, he chased any cats that dared come into the garden. Twice a day he barked fiercely at the postman, as if to say, "I'm not even afraid of postmen."

He was a little bit afraid of the maidservant, Maggie. Especially when she was cross, which was most of the time. Certainly he was afraid of warm water, soap and sponges. In fact, getting a bath from Maggie was the worst thing that had ever happened to him …

Until that terrible day when his master, Mr Scott, brought home a box of fireworks.

Wallace liked the fizzly sparklers and the bright showers of coloured flame that poured from the Roman candles. He jumped about and squeaked with excitement when a rocket went soaring high into the air with a whoosh!

He was less happy about the hot-air balloon. And when a sudden gust of wind sent it drifting across the garden towards him, Wallace decided there were some fireworks he did *not* like.

There was worse to come. Mr Scott had carelessly left the lid off the box of fireworks. A small spark set them all off at once.

Squibs popped and crackers crackled. A thing called a 'whizz-bang' came whizzing over to where Wallace was standing and, just when he thought it was finished, it suddenly went bang! There were 'blue devils' jumping and bursting all over the place, and a frightening crash of splintered glass as a 'thunderflash' hit the greenhouse. Mrs Scott screamed, and Maggie was dancing up and down shouting something about her lovely washing being ruined.

Wallace was so upset that he didn't dare go into the garden for two days, and the cats had a lovely time scratching up all Mr Scott's rows of lettuce.

When he was two years old, Wallace left home and went to work at the Central Fire Station. His job was to run in front of the fire engine, barking loudly to warn people to get out of the way.

He seemed to have forgotten about the fright he got with the fireworks when he was a puppy. But his firemen friends noticed that he was unhappy about noises that sounded like thunderflashes or bangers – a motor-car backfiring, or an extra loud crack from the driver's whip.

When they got to a fire, Wallace would stay with the horses while the firemen got on with their work. What with the roaring of the flames and the hissing of the high-power hoses, the crash of falling timbers and the rumble and rattle of the ladders, the noise was sometimes enough to upset the most stout-hearted animal.

So Wallace's job was to stand guard beside his friends Kelvin and Clyde and try to prevent them from feeling nervous. Whenever there was a specially loud noise Wallace would wag his tail reassuringly and make a nice wuffing noise as if to say, "Don't worry! Everything's all right."

Kelvin and Clyde felt quite safe when they had their brave friend Wallace close by them.

Wallace had a lot of animal friends. Donald pulled the milk cart that called at the Fire Station every morning. There was a little donkey who patiently dragged a cartload of vegetables to the market two days a week: he didn't seem to have any special name.

And of course there was Snowy the Fire Station cat. When Snowy was particularly annoying, Wallace would growl and chase her out of the way, but most of the time they got on well together.

One of Wallace's best friends was a little white poodle called Towser, who was able to walk and dance about on his hind legs. His full name was 'Private Towser' because his master, Mr Wilson, dressed him up in a little kilt and a scarlet jacket to make him look like a Scottish soldier.

The little dancing dog worked at a theatre called the "Scotia Music Hall", not far from the Fire Station. Mr Wilson played the piano accordion and Private Towser danced in time to the music. He also jumped through hoops and pushed a pram that had a real monkey in it.

Not all the acts at the Scotia were as popular as the performing poodle. There was one singer who had a very loud voice and a very red nose. He also sang rather boring songs. The people who went regularly to the Scotia used to hiss and boo whenever he came on the stage.

One evening, when the poor man's nose was even redder than usual, somebody in the audience stood up and shouted "Fire!" It was meant as a joke about his nose, but there was nothing funny about what happened as a result.

Everybody thought the theatre was on fire. They jumped up and started pushing and shoving, jostling and struggling to get through the narrow doorways.

Private Towser and his master were just arriving at the theatre in time for their act, when they were knocked down by a crowd of panic stricken people rushing down from the gallery. Mr Wilson gave a loud yell as somebody trod on his hand. Then somebody else tripped over his legs and fell heavily on top of him. Soon there was a great pile of people, all struggling to get back onto their feet and away from what they thought was a dangerous fire. And at the bottom of the pile was Mr Wilson.

There was a clatter of hooves as Kelvin and Clyde came galloping up the road. The firemen leaped down and started to roll out their hoses, ready to fight the fire.

But of course there *was* no fire. Mr Wilson and six other people had been badly hurt in the crush. The firemen looked after them until the ambulance arrived.

Towser was very upset, but he cheered up a little when he saw Wallace.

The Captain of the fire engine, Mr Paterson, said that Towser had better come back to the Fire Station for a day or two until his master was better.

Mr Paterson's children, Annie and Jimmy, were very excited when they heard that the little poodle from the Scotia was to be their guest.

"Come on Towser", said Annie. "Let's see you do your famous dance."

But, now that all the bustle and excitement was over, Private Towser suddenly felt quite exhausted. He flopped into Wallace's basket. Three seconds later he was fast asleep.

That night Wallace slept in the stall beside Kelvin and Clyde. The straw was soft and clean and had a nice smell. The two big horses, happy to have Wallace close by, snuffled and chomped, munching contentedly. Everybody slept soundly. And, fortunately, there were no more alarm calls that night.

Next morning Wallace introduced Private Towser to all his friends at the Fire Station.

First they paid a visit to Wallace's special friend Mr Gregor. He was too old to go out with the fire engine, but he made all the boots and belts for the other firemen, mended the old leather hoses and kept the harness in good repair.

It was Mr Gregor who had made the two little pairs of leather boots for Wallace, to protect his paws from the hard cobbled streets.

Mr Gregor was so pleased to see Towser dancing that he promised to make some boots for him as well. He said they would make a nice pattering noise as the little dog danced on the stage. They would be much smaller than Wallace's, so he thought he could have them finished by tea time – especially as, unlike Wallace, Towser would only need one pair of boots.

In the afternoon the two dogs played with Jimmy and Annie and the other children who lived at the Fire Station.

'Find Towser' was a good game. One team went rushing off to hide, taking Towser with them, while the other team huddled together with their eyes shut. When they had counted up to a hundred they shouted, "Three, two, one, here we come!" and began to search. Towser got very excited whenever he heard the "Three, two, one, here we come!" call, and danced about, barking happily.

Wallace quickly learned that it was his job to listen for the bark and then to lead the "Wallace Team" to where the "Towser Team" was hiding.

Suddenly the alarm bell rang. Wallace went racing off to the engine shed, giving a growly bark that seemed to say, "No more time for playing. I've got serious work to do."

"Never mind," said Jimmy. "Maybe he'll be back soon for another game."

But it would be a long time before Wallace would play 'Find Towser' again.

The fire at the 'Trongate Waxworks Show' was started by a gang of boys who called themselves 'The Blue Devils'. They chose this name because they like to jump about, making a great deal of noise and giving people frights.

One small spark from one small firework started the biggest fire the people of Glasgow had seen for a long long time.

"Out of the way!" barked Wallace as the fire engine made its way through the crowds of afternoon shoppers. The firemen connected the hoses to the street hydrants, and soon powerful jets of water were sent crashing through the shattered windows into the heart of the burning building. A big extension ladder rattled its way upwards and two firemen clumped their way up to the smouldering roof.

The driver led Kelvin and Clyde over to a quiet spot, away from the noise and bustle, the flying embers and the choking smoke. He didn't need to tell Wallace what his job was.

Indeed the little fire dog was so busy looking after his horse friends that he didn't notice a boy creep up behind him and clip a lighted firecracker to his tail.

The Blue Devils roared with laughter as the startled little dog went whirling round and round, trying to snap free of the fiercely exploding firework. Then they started throwing thunderflashes at him.

There was a blinding flash as one burst near his face. The noise hurt his ears and the hot flame cruelly scorched his fur.

Wallace was terrified. This was the worst thing that had happened to him since that dreadful fireworks day in the garden when he was a puppy.

For the first time in his life he abandoned his post beside Kelvin and Clyde. He went rusing off in a blind panic, and didn't stop until he reached the Fire Station, where he limped up to Mr Gregor and lay down at his feet, quivering with shock and pain.

Wallace seemed better next morning. He did his usual tour of the Fire Station to say hello to all his friends, to sniff at all the nice familiar smells and to see that Snowy was behaving herself.

But when, later on, the alarm bell sounded and the fire engine began to move off, the firemen looked at each other in astonishment.

Where was Wallace? Nobody seemed to know – and of course they couldn't wait to find out.

Annie found him – cowering in the corner of Kelvin's stall. The poor dog was shaking and whimpering, desperately anxious to answer the alarm call and to go running off to catch up with the fire engine, but terrified at the memory of those dreadful fireworks.

Meanwhile the fire engine made its way through the busy streets. The bell clanged, whistles shrilled, the heavy hooves and iron-rimmed wheels clattered and rumbled on the rough cobble-stones. But there was no cheerful patter of leather boots, no happy little dog bounding on ahead to tell everybody that the fire brigade was on its way.

The bystanders watched them go by and missed the familiar figure of the fire dog.

"Where's Wallace got to?"

"Where's thon wee dog with the boots?"

The horses didn't seem to gallop quite so fast without him, and even the big brass bell sounded dull and sad.

The days went by. When Wallace managed to forget about fireworks he felt fine. On Saturday morning he went with the children to the Sugarally Mountains – a piece of waste ground where you could bowl your gird up and down the great heaps of cinders, shale and dross.

In the middle was a pool of filthy water called the Stinky Ocean. It was green and slimy. Bubbles rose to the surface and burst quietly, giving off a stench of rotten eggs. Once Annie had waded in up to her knees to get her ball back and she needed three baths with plenty of soda in the water to get rid of the smell.

Wallace didn't mind the smell of the Stinky Ocean. Running beside the children and their girds wasn't the same as running with the fire engine, but it was good fun. He felt fine.

Jimmy's gird went dirling against a stone and snapped with a sharp crack. When they got home, the fireman who did all the blacksmith jobs at the Fire Station – like mending wheels, shoeing the horses, fitting new shafts to the fire-axes – said that he would fix it.

A few blasts from the bellows set the furnace roaring. Soon the forge rang to the cheerful clink of hammer on anvil, and a shower of sparks cascaded to the floor as the blacksmith struck again and again at the white hot metal.

But Wallace didn't stay to watch. This was too much like a fireworks show. He went slinking off with his tail between his legs.

Monday was Hallow'een, and after tea the children dressed up to go guising. While Mr Paterson carefully fitted the candle into the turnip lantern, his wife used a piece of burnt cork to give Jimmy a pirate beard. Annie, with a tea-cosy on her head, hoped she looked like Private Towser, so she had to get a smart set of whiskers.

"Come on Wallace. You've got to get dressed up too," said Jimmy. "What about putting on your boots?" But, for some reason or other, Wallace would have nothing to do with his boots.

They decided to go to Monteith Row first. They called it 'Lum Hat Street' because of the posh people who lived there.

A very smart maidservant answered the bell. She said "Drat it!" and went to tell her mistress that there were "some very common children at the door". She came back with a penny and said "That's for fireworks. Now be off with you ... and tell your friends they needn't come guising here. I don't want any more muddy feet trailing up and down my clean stairs."

The guisers thanked her politely. Annie wished her a "Happy Hallow'een" and then slid down the bannisters so as not to touch the smart maidservant's clean stairs. When her bottom hit the big wooden knob with a bump she said "Drat it!"

Wallace was already downstairs sitting at the close entrance. Jimmy was worried to notice that he had run down as soon as he heard the maidservant say "fireworks".

The children got a much warmer welcome at the flats in Stockwell Street. At the first one they visited they each got a penny and a piece of coconut tablet as a reward for performing their 'turn'. Jimmy sang a pirate song. Annie told six jokes – and of course did her Private Towser dance.

At the next flat they dooked for apples and played at trying to bite a scone that had been dipped in sticky black treacle. More of the treacle went onto their faces than into their mouths.

Wallace's 'turn' was to clear up all the treacly bits of scone that had dropped to the floor. Wallace always liked to keep a place tidy.

When they visited Granny they were sent to the kitchen sink to wash the treacle off their faces. Then they all sat in front of the fire, drinking tea and telling ghost stories. Granny tipped some chestnuts onto the shovel and set them on the fire to roast. Soon they were hissing and popping all over the place.

"What's wrong with Wallace that he's disappeared under the bed?" asked Granny.

Annie explained, "He's just not very fond of anything that goes pop these days. He'll soon get over it."

But Jimmy was not so sure. Would Wallace ever manage to forget about the Blue Devils and become once more a brave fire dog?

He was soon to find out. As they walked home they heard the urgent clang of the fire bell, the shrill blast of whistles, and the fire engine swept past at full gallop. There had been yet another alarm call from the Scotia Music Hall – and this time it wasn't a false alarm.

By the time the children got to the theatre, clouds of black smoke were billowing out of the front door. The manageress was telling a policeman how the fire had begun.

"We think a corner of the curtain must have brushed against the footlights," she said. "Luckily it was a very sensible audience. There was no panic rush, so everybody got out safely."

Or so she thought.

She was wrong. The actors and actresses had been planning to have a party in the theatre after the show. They had stacked up crates of drinks, trays of cakes and bags of biscuits at the back of the stage. Before he went off to collect the hot pies from the baker, Mr Wilson had left Towser to stand guard over the party food – well away from the biscuits. Now he was trapped.

As the angry flames crept closer, the frightened dog began to bark.

Out in the street, Wallace pricked up his ears. Surely he had heard that bark before? Hadn't there been a game, with the children laughing and calling, "Go on Wallace ... find Towser?"

As Wallace moved towards the theatre entrance, Jimmy called out in alarm, "Hey Wallace! Come back here!"

But already Wallace was inside the burning building.

As the scorching flames reached the wooden crates, the bottles began to burst. It sounded like a box of giant thunderflashes all going off at once.

Wallace was afraid. He turned tail and began to slink away from the noise and the danger.

Then, as Towser's bark turned to a pitiful whine, Wallace stopped. The hair bristled along his back. He was angry at the cruel thing that was happening to his friend. He growled deep in his throat as the anger grew stronger than the fear.

"Hold on Private Towser, hold on! . . . Three, two, one, here I come!" And gathering every ounce of courage and strength, he gave a mighty leap, hurling himself through the deadly wall of smoke and flame and jagged, shattering glass.

With a savage sweep of his fangs Wallace slashed through the rope. The two friends got out just as the roof of the theatre fell in with a sickening crash.

Annie wept bitterly when she saw Wallace. His fur was badly singed, his paws torn and bleeding. Blood was oozing from two bad cuts on his side. Jimmy was just about bursting with pride.

"Come on, here! Let's go home and look after your wounds."

But Wallace had other things on his mind. Calmly making his way through the cheering crowd, he took up his old post beside Kelvin and Clyde.

"All right then friends," he seemed to be saying. "Settle down now and stop worrying."

Wallace the fire dog was back on duty.

The next day was November the fifth – Fireworks Day – and the alarm bell at the Fire Station scarcely stopped ringing. Wallace and the firemen were just back from a fire caused by a rocket landing on a pile of straw in a cowshed, when another call came through.

"Warehouse at Sugarally Mountains. Bonfire out of control."

The Blue Devils were there, looking for more mischief.

"Look!" shouted the leader, lighting a thunderflash. "There's the dog that's afraid of fireworks. This'll be fun!"

It was fun ... but not for the Blue Devils. Wallace gave just one warning growl and then exploded into action like the biggest thunderflash that ever was.

The boys didn't stop running until they were wallowing about helplessly in the oozy slime of the Stinky Ocean.

Wallace stood by, happily panting and wagging his tail, as Jimmy's father gave the boys a long lecture about how dangerous fireworks could be.

"Learn sense," he warned, "before you blow off some of your fingers, or blind yourselves, or kill somebody."

The boys didn't feel much like blue devils any more – more like green squelches. They were afraid of the angry fireman. They were even more afraid of the fierce dog. But most of all they were afraid of what their mothers would do to them when they went home smelling like a cartload of rotten eggs.

That evening old Mr Gregor set off the children's fireworks. Everybody enjoyed the display and nobody got hurt. Wallace was out with the fire engine all evening, but he managed to look in between alarm calls – just to see that everything was being done properly.

In spite of his bandage and some scorched patches on his fur, he looked very smart, with his brightly polished boots gleaming in the light of the fireworks.

As Towser went dancing up to meet him, he seemed to be saying, "This is my friend Wallace ... he's the bravest dog in Glasgow."